Praise for Huckleberries and Coyotes

Dr. Michelle Jacob shares contemporary Indigenous stories full of love and connection, giving an inside look at how Tribal communities continue to engage in culture and story. After reading the stories, you will walk away with a new appreciation for Mother Earth and our more than human relations.

—Mercedes Jones, Confederated Tribes of Grand Ronde, Curriculum Specialist

Michelle Jacob has perfectly captured both the fine craft and the deep meanings essential to the Yakama story tradition. This is what she asks of us: read and listen, take great pleasure, think hard, learn. And then seek out good life, humbly attentive to that greater world that surrounds us. *Huckleberries and Coyotes* is a lovely journey but also perfectly attuned to the challenges of a dark time.

—Dr. Philip J. Deloria, Harvard University

This book is an achievement. It is intergenerational and multi-audience. The storytelling is polished, skillful, and deft. The writing really reflects a talent for weaving together themes, philosophies, and prompts in ways that are simultaneously ancient, everyday, contemporary, and brutally honest. I appreciated the mix of traditional and non-traditional species as well as the layers of life experiences across ecosystems, from gathering places, shopping places, domestic places, and agricultural places, among others.

—Dr. Kyle Whyte (Citizen Potawatomi Nation), Michigan State University

Huckleberries and Coyotes is a joy to read, so beautifully written and readily relatable. I love this book and the value it has for catalyzing learning.

—Dr. Regina Sievert, American Indian Higher Education Consortium

Huckleberries and Coyotes is a lovely book that reminds us of our connections with each other, land and place, and our more-than-human relatives. As a professor who teaches about the importance of learning from and with our place and the land, I plan to use this book in my classes as well as with my own children. In *Huckleberries and Coyotes*, Dr. Jacob beautifully demonstrates a way to Indigenize our educational practices.

—Dr. Stephany RunningHawk Johnson (Oglala Lakota), Washington State University

Huckleberries and Coyotes is alive with imagery and language that reach through the stories to delight and inspire readers of all ages. The stories invite us to be present with ourselves and our more than human teachers. *Huckleberries and Coyotes* will stay with you and call you back to visit again and again.

—Dr. Tina Gutierez-Schmich, Equity Director, Bethel School District

Michelle Jacob's collection of short stories, *Huckleberries and Coyotes: Lessons from Our More than Human Relations*, provides 12 windows into old and new ways of being in relationship with the world around you. As a teacher of teachers, I see this book as useful on both a personal and professional level. Personally, the stories and journal writing prompts allow teachers to activate their own creative thinking and ability to connect to story and personal meaning. Professionally, teachers of science, geography, literature, language, and social studies can make use of these stories in engaging students in connections to land, life, language, culture, and community.

—Dr. Julia Heffernan, Graduate Director of Curriculum and Instruction, University of Oregon

Also by Michelle M. Jacob

Yakama Rising: Indigenous Cultural Revitalization, Activism, and Healing

Indian Pilgrims: Indigenous Journeys of Activism and Healing with Saint Kateri Tekakwitha

On Indian Ground: A Return to Indigenous Knowledge: Generating Hope, Leadership, and Sovereignty through Education in the Northwest (co-edited with Stephany RunningHawk Johnson)

The Auntie Way: Stories Celebrating Kindness, Fierceness, and Creativity

Huckleberries and Coyotes

Lessons from Our More than Human Relations

Written by

Michelle M. Jacob

Illustrated by

Crystal L. Buck

ANAHUY MENTORING, LLC

EXCELLENCE IN INDIGENOUS METHODS

Author royalties are donated to the Sapsik'ʷałá Program at the University of Oregon to support the next generation of Indigenous teachers. By purchasing this book, you are supporting Indigenous self-determination in education. Kw'ałanúushamash! (I am grateful to you!)

ISBN (paperback): 978-1-7346151-2-8

ISBN (e-book): 978-1-7346151-3-5

Cover design & layout: Christopher J. Andersen

Cover illustration: Crystal Buck

Library of Congress Control Number: 2020913999

Copyright © 2020 Anahuy Mentoring, LLC

Whitefish, MT

https://anahuymentoring.com

Twitter: @AnahuyMentoring

This book is dedicated to all of our teachers and relatives who gather and prepare our traditional foods. Your work is a blessing that connects us to place and nourishes our bodies and spirits.

Contents

Introduction

Welcome. I am glad you are here.

This book is an invitation to learn from key Indigenous teachings:

1) the importance of place,

2) the importance of being in good relation with ourselves and with all beings,

3) the power of stories as teaching and learning tools.

I was inspired to write this book because I have witnessed the power of stories in my community. Stories are gifts from Elders and are precious narratives that hold within them a loving and caring vision for our people and anyone who wishes to learn.

Stories teach us how to conduct ourselves,

how to take care of ourselves and one another, how to pay attention to our surroundings, and how to be in good relation with our fellow humans and all beings.

These precious teachings, which have been with us Since Time Immemorial, and carried and shared from generation to generation, extend back to our creation story, in which humans did not yet exist, but the Earth was already peopled—with Salmon People, Water People, and so on. Indeed, Salmon and Water offered themselves as gifts so that pitiful humans could exist, and we became closely related to Salmon. Often Indigenous peoples from across the Pacific Northwest will refer to ourselves as Salmon People or part of the Salmon Nation. Similarly, our sacred Huckleberry is not just a *food*; rather, Elders explain she is our *sister*. We have a responsibility to *all* of our relatives, human and more than human. When we reflect on the meaning and importance of our many relations who surround us and sustain life on Mother Earth, we are better able to sense our responsibilities to live our best lives.

Huckleberries and Coyotes: Lessons from Our More than Human Relations is a contemporary expression of the timeless Indigenous tradition of storytelling. Our people's stories are precious educational curricula. Storytelling traditionally takes place communally in wintertime gatherings. Yet in our lives, we face so many challenges and changes. At the time of this writing, it is not safe for Elders to gather with large groups of people to tell stories due to the pandemic we are all facing. Our people have always adapted our traditions for the contemporary times, and I hope that this book serves as a helpful resource for our people and all peoples who wish to engage with stories to learn and grow.

In this collection, I share with you stories that connect you to places of importance to me; some take place on my Indigenous homeland, and some take place where I've been a guest or visitor. In a time when climate change, bigotry, racism, sexism, and the challenges of grief and loss threaten our physical, mental, and spiritual well-being, stories have the potential to help us heal.

Stories can teach us the transformative power of the collective. This is serious business. Yet the stories in *Huckleberries and Coyotes* are also light-hearted and fun. They are observations of everyday life, and an invitation for you to both laugh heartily and think deeply. Each story is accompanied by discussion/journaling questions to help you engage with the story's deeper meanings as well as tap into your inner wisdom.

Each reader brings a unique perspective to each story, and it is my hope that all readers will find both entertainment and nourishment by engaging with these stories, whether you are reading this book on your own or as part of a group.

Time and again, our stories reaffirm the power we have in working as a collective. I hope that you are able to share your own wisdom, through storytelling and discussion, with those who are important in your life. We all benefit when this happens.

Thank you for joining me in learning lessons from our more than human relations.

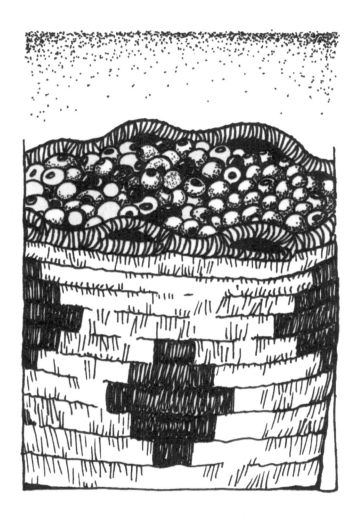

I Love Wíwnu (Huckleberry)

I love Wíwnu. She's sweet. And petite. And *just* a bit tart. Kind of like Auntie.

I remember Auntie praying over us and offering a blessing before we went Wíwnu picking at the lake up at the base of Pátu (Mount Adams) in our gorgeous Cascade Mountains. Auntie was already an Elder with gray hair neatly permed and set under a head scarf. But she was strong and determined and could thrive on that hill beside the lake. Just like Wíwnu.

I remember Auntie taking her basket and climbing up that hill—so high she was just a dot.

"Look at her! She's like a mountain goat!" Dad said, while puffing on his cigar, taking a short break from fishing. He stood and watched her climb farther up, and then Dad turned and effortlessly threw another cast into the lake, his fishing reel spinning zzzzzzzzzzzzzzz with delight, bobber almost instantly signaling another rainbow trout (x̲úlx̲ul).

I had helped Auntie pick Wíwnu in the easy-to-reach bushes lower down by the lake. It was hard to get comfortable crouching in place, picking just the ripe purple berries, no stems or leaves, please! We only want the berries. A tremendous effort of skill but mostly patience. It seemed like *forever* before I was able to fill the bottom layer of my basket. This was just a few handfuls of ripe berries! A quantity I could easily eat in about 1.5 seconds. Auntie encouraged me, though, and complimented me on the lack of leaves and stems in my basket. "Those will be easy to clean and use later," she reminded me. We all knew the tedious task of cleaning berries from a sloppy picker: the slow work of finding and removing all the stem and leaf debris. How quickly we'd like to condemn such a picker as immoral: thoughtless, selfish, in a hurry—some of the most vicious insults we could think of.

"No, no," Auntie would intervene. "You must think kind and good thoughts when you're handling our sacred foods. Wíwnu is your sister. You're harming her if you say harsh things or hold bad feelings around her."

"Yes, Auntie. I'm sorry." We'd quickly get back on track, stepping into our better selves.

Of course, most of the berries were easy to clean, as they'd come from Auntie's huge berry basket she repeatedly filled, gallons and gallons of berries. Her many decades of practice picking Huckleberries made her a true expert; yet she always had patience, encouragement, and kind words for beginners who struggled to fill even the smallest basket or bag.

Auntie's lessons stay with us. Her spirit soars like the eagle gliding near the hills where she used to pick Wíwnu. Every time I taste Wíwnu, I remember her: sweet, petite, and *just* a bit tart. I love my Auntie. And I love Wíwnu.

Note: For more Auntie stories, please check out *The Auntie Way: Stories Celebrating Kindness, Fierceness, and Creativity* (Anahuy Mentoring, 2020). More information is at the end of this book.

Discussion/Journaling Questions for "I Love Wíwnu (Huckleberry)"

1. In "I Love Wíwnu," the narrator shares a lesson to not say harsh things or hold bad feelings. Think of a time when you learned a similar lesson. Who or what helped teach you in that situation? What is important from the lesson that you continue to carry with you today?

2. Think of a person you love whom you associate with a special food. What is a specific memory you have about that person and the food?

3. In "I Love Wíwnu," the berry picking place is important as a site that holds memories and where important lessons were learned. What is a place that is important to you—for holding memories and for where important lessons were learned?

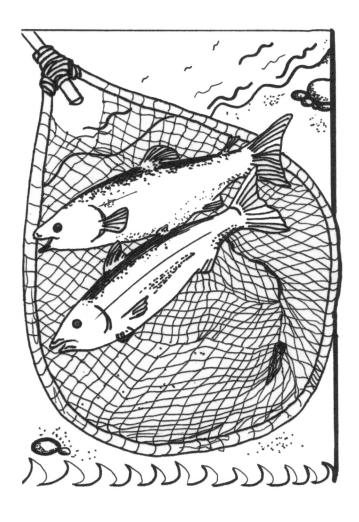

Silver Beauty

The silver skin
of Salmon dancing
in my brother's fishing net,

more beautiful
than silver jewelry
I once spied
through a window in Santa Fe,

more beautiful
than the flash of silver
at cocktail parties
fingers and wrists glinting
as glasses clink
in spirited toasts.

Our silver beauty, dancing in the net,
timeless,
priceless,
sacred.

Despite their mild protest
give their blessing
respecting the ancient covenant;
allowing our existence.

Our past, present, future
always interwoven
with the
beautiful silver People.

Discussion/Journaling Questions for "Silver Beauty"

1. In "Silver Beauty," the narrator references the creation story in which Salmon stepped forward as a food offering so that humans could live; this was during the time before humans existed, and Creator asked all the living beings if any would sacrifice themselves so that the pitiful humans could exist. This "ancient covenant" reminds the narrator of the gratitude owed to Salmon, who were among the First People to populate Mother Earth long before humans arrived. In what ways do you feel gratitude toward food? How might the world be different if humility and gratitude toward food were more deeply embraced?

2. Think of a food you find to be beautiful. What specifically about this particular food do you find beautiful?

3. Think of one of your favorite beautiful foods. Whose Indigenous land or water does this food come from? On whose help do you rely to obtain this food?

Yellow Bell Is Beautiful

One of my favorite traditional Yakama stories stars the delightful, relatable, likable, fantastic character Yellow Bell (Síkni). Yellow Bell is the youngest of the spring flower sisters, and she gets into trouble in the story because she sleeps in and doesn't give herself enough time to properly groom and prepare herself for the beginning of spring—which leads her to be late, and on top of that, she has a sloppy, messy appearance.

Now, this is not to say that it's our highest cultural value to preen and groom ourselves with painstaking care or, as my dad says, to "kiss oneself in the mirror until your lips turn blue!"

No.

Rather, the story is about the importance of

having respect for yourself, taking care of yourself, and being prepared to greet the day and all your relations. It is also about being thoughtful of others so you don't cause chaos when they have to wait for you.

It's about being "in time" (as opposed to a hypervigilant watching-the-clock "on time").

When I was a student organizing powwows, we printed a note in the program: Our culture values being "in time" more than being "on time." We printed that to help calm the nerves of tourists and visitors who may have gotten anxious if Grand Entry was running five minutes late.

But there are limits to how late one can be and still be "in time." Yellow Bell learns this in the story, and she continues to teach us this today. You can find her with her head drooping humbly as she acknowledges: Yes, I was late. Yes, I was sloppy. Yes, I was inconsiderate by making everyone wait for me.

Yellow Bell is so lovable. Kind of lazy, kind of sloppy. Yet ultimately, she's intensely humble and dedicates herself to teaching us, so we may be better and do better. Like all kind and loving teachers, she helps us step into our better selves.

Yellow Bell is beautiful.

Note: A more comprehensive telling of "The Wild Spring Flowers" is in *Anakú Iwachá*, published in 1974; the legend is also included in the second edition of *Anakú Iwachá* (University of Washington Press, 2021).

Discussion/Journaling Questions for "Yellow Bell Is Beautiful"

1. One of the reasons why Yellow Bell is so lovable is that she is relatable with her sloppiness and laziness. Think of someone you admire greatly and the flaws that they occasionally show. What about them do you admire? How might their flaws make them more relatable?

2. In the story "Yellow Bell Is Beautiful," readers are encouraged to consider the difference between being "in time" versus "on time." What does the difference between these two concepts mean to you? When might you prefer to be "in time" versus "on time"?

3. Yellow Bell learned an important and difficult teaching about being honest and taking responsibility for one's actions. She becomes a model of accountability for us all. Describe a time when you or someone you know learned a lesson about being responsible, accountable, or honest. What did you learn from that lesson? How does it influence your thinking and behavior today?

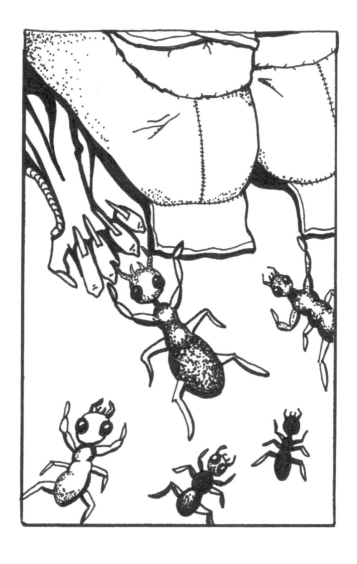

Ants Are Special Beings

Ants are special beings. They're crafty and strong. If you've ever seen an ant carry away a potato chip five times the ant's size, you know what I mean.

I've heard Indigenous traditional stories that teach how ants are responsible for helping save human beings from destruction. What responsibility and dignity those small beings have.

In my own Yakama cultural teachings, ants have a special place. They are the originators of the Plateau-style moccasins we wear. The explanation for this is contained in our story about Wormface, a handsome man who deceives people with his appearance; he is actually a monster with worms crawling out of his face, but he hides under a handsome facade. Wormface uses charm and deceptive good looks to trick a conceited young woman into marrying him, despite the protests of the woman's family, who didn't trust the strange man. Worm-face's true intention is to use his young wife as food for his monster mother, and his new bride finds this out soon after they depart her village. She begins to regret not listening to her loved ones and becomes miserable on the journey with her monster husband.

In the story, ants witness the misery of the young woman, and they take pity on her. Ants instruct her to secretly sew a flap on the bottom of each of her moccasins' heels. Then, when the woman and her husband reach the lake where his monster mother lives, Wormface tries to throw his wife in to feed the monster mother, but he is unable to, despite his great strength. After several attempts, the monster mother instructs Wormface to let his bride go, as she clearly has special powers. Wormface and his mother didn't realize ants held the woman firmly rooted in place by their tight grasp of the moccasins' flaps, their ant collective superpower strength saving the day.

At a recent telling of this story, a wise man shared that it is a cautionary tale; you never know who Wormface will be, a deceptive monster that threatens to destroy you—maybe it's drugs, or alcohol, or pride. I nodded my head in agreement with this wise counsel.

Upon reflection, I see another layer. It's true we never know who Wormface might be. We also never know who the ants might be. Ants are special beings who can save the day with their thoughtfulness, innovation, and collective strength. May we all be a little more ant-like today.

Note: A more comprehensive telling of the "Legend about Wormface" is in *Anakú Iwachá*, a precious collection of Yakama stories first published in 1974; the legend is also included in the second edition of *Anakú Iwachá* (University of Washington Press, 2021).

Discussion/Journaling Questions for
"Ants Are Special Beings"

1. Ants are small but strong. Think of someone who is stronger than you first thought, especially when they work with others. What do you learn from this person and the way they show their strength?

2. In the story of Wormface, the conceited young woman was only concerned about outer appearances. Think of a time when you were concerned with a surface-level issue or appearance. How did you learn the deeper meaning and lesson? How do you carry this wisdom with you, and act upon it, today?

3. In the story above, ants are noted as thoughtful, innovative, and collectively strong. Think of a time when you embodied these traits. What is a situation in your life in which you could be more ant-like? Brainstorm a plan for being so—you've got this!

Playing and Praying

Satiny soft to the touch.

Yet strong enough to tumble you head over feet, over head over feet, if you're caught in a breaking wave.

Boiling hot, you can burn yourself, perhaps needing to be rushed to the hospital.

Yet when you've been working outside in the blazing sun and are parched inside and out, its refreshing coolness is a miracle, a blessing.

You drink it up.

You must. To survive.

Just like the 100-foot-tall trees you admire in the forest.

The wise Protectors say, "Water is Life," and they are right.

We all rely on the precious gift, including my dog, whose collar tags clang against his metal bowl as he slurp-drinks with his long pink tongue.

Clang, clang, clang, the noise goes, similar to the mission bells I remember from my time on Luiseño/Payómkawichum, Juaneño/Acjachemen, Chumash, and Kumeyaay/Tipai-Ipai homelands, all strong and resilient Indigenous peoples with beautiful cultures who survived waves of colonization—outsiders who lusted for Indigenous peoples' lands and sought to eradicate the "Indian problem."

But the people remain. Proud resistors who have kept their sacred relationship with land and water intact.

Water—a holy gift to us from the Creator.

Among my own Yakama people, we revere Water and give prayers of gratitude:

When we look upon glaciers atop our sacred mountains.

When we fish, or skim rocks with young ones, at our lakes and creeks.

When we play in the sprinkler or the bright yellow slip and slide atop the lawn on those hot summer days.

When we belly flop into the city pool our Tribal Nation pays to operate so we have a healthy activity during summer break.

When we drive to Portland to go shopping or catch the airplane; we see our traditional fishermen and fisherwomen working on our behalf along Nch'i Wána (the Columbia River), maintaining the ancient covenant among the First People (Salmon and Water) and us, the pitiful human people, who cannot live without our generous relatives who feed us and quench our thirst.

We pray with Water before each sacred meal, acknowledging our debt and love to the holy being—Water.

Chuush!

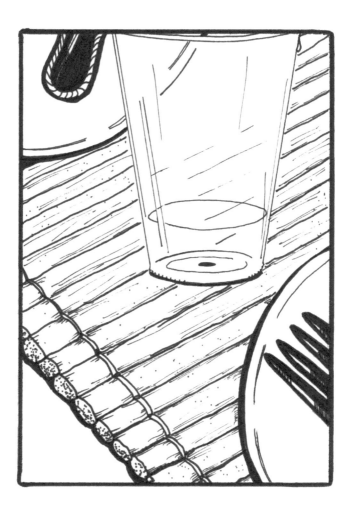

Discussion/Journaling Questions for "Playing and Praying"

1. Think of a time when you played in the water. What were you doing and how did you feel? When might you play in water next?

2. In "Playing and Praying," the narrator mentions the wisdom of the Water Protectors, who say "Water is Life." Where does your fresh water come from? How are you helping to protect your own water source? If you are unsure, do one small task to educate yourself to become involved.

3. In "Playing and Praying," the narrator mentions the humility of humans, who depend on so many "generous relatives." Which other beings do you depend on to survive? Name at least 10 you depended on today (hint: water and air are two!). Savor how fortunate you are to have such generous relatives.

Reclaiming Apple

Fall is a beautiful time of year, perhaps the most beautiful. The leaves change. The hot summer nights finally become cool.

And apples ripen, ready to be the star in some of my favorite fall-time treats.

Apple pie, still warm from the oven, with a buttery flakey crust, a dollop of ice cream melting just a bit, and those tender slices of apples inside that smell like fall.

Or fresh pressed apple cider. I pick it up at the farm stand and love deciding: drink it as a cold refreshing taste of fall during a warm sunny afternoon or wait and drink it steaming hot from a mug on a chilly night?

Or the smell of my homemade applesauce filling my home as I cook a big pot of it on our stove;

it has cinnamon and ginger highlights. I leave the skin on to make it a lovely blush color when I blend it up before placing it in jars, ready to take to Elders when I visit.

Apples are special to me. I've been friends with this fruit my whole life.

I remember, when I was six years old, the ache in my back from carrying a heavy load of apples in my picking bag. How my dad had to cinch the straps up high so the bag would better fit me and not drag on the ground. How I'd reach up for apples on the appointed tree, fill my bag as full as I could—not nearly as full as my brothers', but like in all things, I did my best to imitate them. I wasn't a great help in the apple picking tasks, but I was encouraged and welcomed to join in the family labor, their kindness affirming my small contributions to the greater collective.

Once my bag was full, I'd waddle, my back stooped with effort, over to the bin we were to fill as fast as we could. The empty bin looked *enormous* to me. How would we ever fill it? Yet I knew somehow it was possible—I'd seen the semi-truck trailers with full bins of apples stacked neatly like Legos and headed to the warehouse by Highway 97. I'd seen my dad drive the old, mustard-colored forklift and maneuver those bins weighing a thousand pounds each, full of the literal fruits of our family's labor.

I was not yet tall enough to hoist my picking bag over the bin's edge to deposit my freshly picked apples into the collective pile. So, I climbed the step my dad had specially welded for me; he took the time to make the special step so that I would be able to be in the orchard and help out alongside the rest of our family. You could always tell which bin I was helping with because my little step was latched on the side of the bin, kind of like the kitchen cabinet towel bar I own today, with its hooks in place atop the cabinet door in front of the kitchen sink. Once I climbed the step, I unhooked the knotted rope that held fast my bag. The bag released and apples tumbled freely out the bottom of my bag into the bin. Then I fixed my bag back into its carrying vessel shape, hooking the knotted rope on each side into the metal holder so no apples would fall on the ground as I picked and filled my next load.

I remember the chorus of instructions when I tried to work too quickly. Careful! When you pick, keep the stem attached but no leaves! We don't want leaves in the bin.

I looked up at the tall tree I'd been working on. So many apples! How would we pick them all? But of course, we did. Tree by tree. Row by row. Acre by acre. Until the entire 80 acres my parents had planted before my birth were picked.

Apples are not a traditional Indigenous food for Yakamas. But what do you do with a rectangular piece of land on a poor and rural reservation? My parents chose to farm the family's allotment. No one in our family had ever planted an orchard. But my parents saw orchards thriving across the river, off the reservation, and thought, "Why not?" Eventually my dad quit his job at the Indian agency and farmed full time, a job with no weekends off, no reliable downtime, without the security of an hourly wage.

Later in life, I would learn the process of planting an orchard. The clearing and tilling of the land, hard work done by my dad and oldest brothers. Then huge burn piles to clear all the debris. This was the era before burn bans arrived to our reservation. Next, neat rows were plowed. Finally, the little skinny sticks arrived from the nursery, and it was all hands on deck, at least on as much of a deck that the big tractor had, with one tractor driver, usually Dad, and one tree seedling minder, one of the kids, who'd pass the stick trees to the planter, another kid, one at a time in a rhythmic motion. Grab-Pass-Plant. Grab-Pass-Plant. So the symphony of orchard planting went as the tractor coasted along in a neat straight line. Two other kids would follow behind, making sure the stick trees were covered over at the roots with soil.

Once done with the large chore, we admired our brand-new baby trees and how they stood at attention, ready and waiting to grow and thrive, to hopefully win battles: against the elements and pests, sure, but also the seeming more distant battles such as irrigation water rights, the availability of labor, access to credit, and the tastes of consumers who would browse the varieties of apples in the supermarket, six years in the future, when this newly planted orchard would finally be coming into full production.

Today when I do my own supermarket browsing, sometimes I pause and look at the multicolored display of apples. Such variety! All those piles sitting there—shiny with wax and each (nowadays) donning a sticker to show their provenance. Sometimes I read the stickers and think about all the hands that have touched those apples. The long journeys they've made to sit in a pile before me, for my consuming pleasure. The farmers who, six to ten years ago, took a gamble with their family's financial well-being and ordered *this* particular variety of tree seedling, likely persuaded by sugar content, skin color, resistance to bruising, and shelf life.

All of the apples grown in the United States come from Indigenous homeland. For those grown on reservations, they likely come from land that is allotted, either currently or previously, into tidy rectangular shapes, 80 acres at a time, the work of government surveyors and a U.S. Congress eager to gobble up Indigenous land holdings. U.S. laws were created to designate huge swaths of Indigenous homeland as "surplus" and ready to be thrown open to settlement, sold at bargain basement prices for white men to build their futures; such is the legacy of settler colonialism.

Apple is sometimes used as a derogatory term for Native Americans ("red on the outside, white on the inside" goes the racialized joke).

Yet based on my experience, I think we should perhaps reclaim the term. I see how our people and cultures have all the best traits sought in apples: sweetness, beautiful varying skin color, resilience against the bruisings of life, and persistent shelf life, for sure.

Apples. These sphere-shaped fruits, they are sturdy little miracles.

And so are we.

Discussion/Journaling Questions for "Reclaiming Apple"

1. Pick one of your favorite seasons. What are special foods you enjoy during this season? What are activities (either leisure or work related) that you associate with this season? Describe a special time when you really enjoyed taking part in seasonal activities.

2. In "Reclaiming Apple," apples are described as "sturdy little miracles." What is one of your favorite foods you think of as sturdy or miraculous? On whose Indigenous homeland does your chosen food grow? Do some research to learn about the history of that land, the resilience of Indigenous peoples in that place, and the water that nourishes the land and the people. We are all connected through history, geography, and the economy. Learning about the ways our food connects us enriches our lives and allows us to be in more respectful relationship with place.

3. In "Reclaiming Apple," the narrator notes how family members are strong role models in their collective work on the farm. Who is one of your role models, today or in the past, who inspires or encourages you? Write a note to thank them. If possible, send the note.

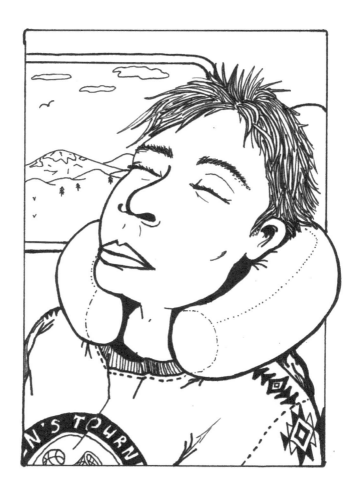

The Color of Tired

I feel tired today.

Tired like a student during finals week trying to stay awake in the 24-hour reading room at the library, praying the all-night vigil with thick textbooks can atone for weeks of procrastination and neglect. Wondering about the long-term effects of chugging Mountain Dew. If it's sugar free, does that help or make it worse?

Bone-achingly tired.

Like the time I flew halfway around the world from India to California. So tired my stomach hurts, and I can't tell whether I'm hungry or not, but perhaps it doesn't matter because none of the food smells good inside the San Francisco airport while I await my next flight. I think I'll try to walk to the end of the terminal again so I don't fall asleep and miss my flight.

Tired.

Like the time I got home and it had snowed at least a foot, so I shoveled the driveway and sidewalk. And after I ate dinner and was headed to bed to rest my sore shoulders, arms, and back, I noticed it had snowed another foot. Boots back on, find my gloves, grab the shovel; yes, I'm tired, but rest can wait.

Tired.

To me, being tired has its own color, its own shade. It's the color of juniper berries when they're young. My whole life, my emotions, my thoughts all turn a shade of grayish green when I'm tired.

But as I turn this idea over in my mind, I see that not all tiredness is the same. There are deeper and lighter shades. Some are dustier looking and feeling. And then I recall that some feelings of tiredness are the deep purple shade of mature juniper berries. For me, and I'm thankful for this, such a state is rare. That kind of tired is at a whole other level.

Like waiting overnight at the hospital while your loved one lies still as a statue in a hospital bed in the ER, connected to a bewildering array of tubes and machines.

At times like these, I find comfort in the image of young juniper berries in my hands. I recall an Elder in the Southwest who explained juniper berries have healing and protective powers. How beautiful that is, to know these berries, whose colors have always struck me as rich and unique, are sacred. Like all sacred beings, they stand at the ready to help those who respectfully ask.

Maybe I can pass some young juniper berries around to my family. We could all then find a moment of near-peace, rolling a berry around in our palms, like those pocket games kids used to play with—turning it this way and that, trying to get that shiny silver ball in the right place.

Maybe we could sneak into our loved one's area, pull back the curtain, and place a juniper berry under the pillow. You see, now we're all connected. We each have a dusty little pea-looking sphere to help us. I hope it will be enough.

Rolling the juniper berry between my thumb and forefinger, I feel silly now, recalling how much I complained during that airport layover. Everyone, clench your berry tightly in your hand, the doctor is coming to talk with us!

I hope we are enough.

When faced with a loved one battling for their life, I yearn for the simpler, easier, dusty gray-green problems in the spectrum of a final exam, a wait for a flight, a pile of snow.

These little berries, they've shared a powerful message with me today. They've given me perspective and hope for protection and healing.

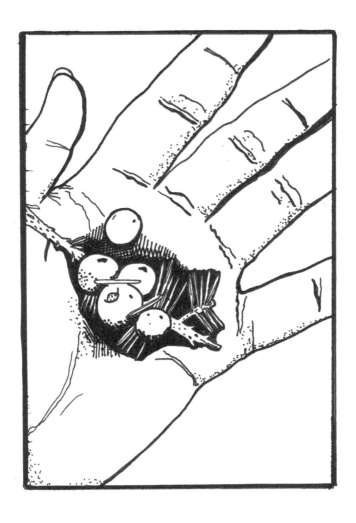

Discussion/Journaling Questions for "The Color of Tired"

1. In "The Color of Tired," the narrator shares the colors she associates with being tired. What colors do you feel and see when you are tired? Can you think of a plant or other being in that color, which may then help you through times when you are feeling tired?

2. In "The Color of Tired," the narrator describes feeling tired from worry at the hospital. If you were the patient in the hospital bed, how would you want your loved ones to feel? What plant or other being would you send to them to help them through that worrying time?

3. The narrator describes being taught that juniper berries are healing and protective. What plant or other being or item do you associate with healing and protection? Discuss one or more ways that you can become closer to this being or item in your daily life, to help you and your loved ones.

Humble and Regal

There is a humble vegetable known as carrot. I love carrot. Such a sturdy vegetable, with that ability to stay in the drawer of the refrigerator and not get slimy or moldy. A tough, enduring being. Like a marathon runner.

I have fond family memories wrapped up with carrots. My grandpa used to grow them in his large vegetable garden at his old house *right* next to the train tracks on the reservation. When I was little, I was terrified of those loud engines and the rumble and noise of heavy train cars going by. *Long* trains. Too many cars to count. I'd cover my ears and curl up in a little ball, hiding from the train monster. Anything that loud must be a monster somehow.

And then, finally, the quiet resumed.

"Have a carrot," my grandpa would say.

And so, we'd munch on carrots, freshly pulled from Mother Earth. Their sweet crispness cheering us both as we sat in lawn chairs, you know the kind, those economical ones with the aluminum frames and woven webbing that could be replaced if needed. They folded in half for storage through the winter, hanging neatly in grandpa's shed. As we munched, he stared off into the distance, his eyes beginning to cloud from cataracts.

"Still afraid of trains, are you," he commented, more than asked.

I nodded in agreement.

"Well, that's understandable. They're big. And loud. You know, one time one jumped the track and came crashing through the living room," he stroked his scruffy facial hair as he told the story.

Grandpa could exaggerate, I knew. But I also knew he was telling a true story at that time. My mom had verified it on a previous occasion, explaining why grandpa's chair was now in a different place than when she was young; now the TV was in the spot where the engine had come crashing through the house. No one had been hurt, thank goodness.

We finished our carrots and decided to watch *The Price Is Right,* our favorite show. Maybe someone will win a car today!

Later, when my first nephew was born, my grandpa's hearing had become worse. He could catch bits of conversation, but unfamiliar words or names were difficult. This is why he called my nephew "Carrot" and commented to me, while shaking his head in mild disapproval, that my brother and sister-in-law had chosen a strange name for their son.

My grandpa lived a long life. He died when my nephew was a toddler. Later, when my nephew was a little older, I'd go with my brother and oldest nephew, Garret, to dig wild carrots (Sawítk) in the foothills of our reservation. Sawítk is more tender and flavorful than the big, bright orange carrots in a plastic bag in the grocery store.

Sawítk takes more effort to gather. She is not available for purchase by the pound at the grocery store. She connects us to land, to place. We are required to touch Mother Earth to harvest Sawítk.

After digging up another wild carrot, I pause for a moment and see the lesson, the gift—a more tender and flavorful life also requires me to slow down and show gratitude to Mother Earth and the treasures all around me.

Up in the foothills, there are no trains roaring by. There is no TV game show. But the experience is in some ways similar to when I was a little girl sitting with my grandfather.

Once again, I found myself first digging gently, then pulling fresh carrots from Mother Earth, brushing them off, and enjoying the sweet, earthy goodness of this humble and regal vegetable.

Discussion/Journaling Questions for "Humble and Regal"

1. Have you ever pulled or dug up a vegetable from Mother Earth? Describe what that experience was like or what you imagine it to be like.

2. Think of someone you know who exaggerates. How do you know when they are telling the "truth"? In what circumstances does it matter to you whether they are telling the "truth" or just a version of the truth?

3. What is a food or tradition that connects generations of your family (whether blood-related family or chosen family such as friends)? Describe the food or tradition and what it means to you. What have you learned through your participation? If you have no such food or tradition, how might you imagine it? Perhaps you can start a tradition—if so, what would you choose?

Daffodils and Stoplight

It's early February and the daffodils are already up. I saw them this morning, groups of spring's yellow soldiers standing tall upon their green stems, proudly announcing that warmer, sunnier weather was on its way.

Yet how could this be? It's early February!

Where I come from this is supposed to be frozen winter weather time.

I notice Áan (sun) is out and he's been ever so present this winter.

Old-timers agree this has been a strangely warm winter. Our Elders, who know the patterns of our seasons and lands best, are deeply concerned about the changes we're seeing. The climate changes. Can our sacred foods survive these changes? Can we? Humans seem to be on a reckless path toward destruction.

Elders are not alone in their concern. Even middle- and young-timers know that what we're experiencing is different.

It's warmer.

Storms are more drastic.

Just like the political climate we're experiencing.

Daffodils blooming in early February.

Cause for celebration?

Or cause for concern?

Just like the stoplight in town, yellow is the color of warning: think carefully about what you will do next. Now that I'm looking for them, I see those yellow clumps everywhere I look.

Spring is a season of renewal. These bright yellow flowers are urging us to more deeply embrace integrity and respect.

Discussion/Journaling Questions for "Daffodils and Stoplight"

1. In "Daffodils and Stoplight," the narrator describes climate change and urges readers to "think carefully about what you do next." What do you think society's response to climate change should be? How will you respond in your own life?

2. The narrator encourages readers to think of the drastic contemporary political climate and consider whether now should be a time for celebration or concern. What do you think we should be celebrating? What is of concern to you? When you discuss matters of importance with someone who has a very different political view, how can you model the importance of integrity and respect?

3. Spring is often a time of renewal and hope. What would you like to renew in your own life? What is your greatest hope at this time?

Best Friends

I love my dog so much. I remember the day I picked him out at the rescue shelter. Or maybe I should say he picked me out. His adorable brown eyes peering into my soul from behind his chain-link cage. It was a magical moment of connection, when all discomfort around us faded to the background— the loud sounds of barking and crying echoing off the shelter's cement walls and floor, the smells of animal musk, pee, poo, and cleaning products all battling it out. All of that vanished as he etched his name onto my heart and mine onto his: instant best friends.

Then, once decided he was the one, I took down the paper posted outside his cage. I read it over quickly. I glanced back at him. He seemed nervous. I turned the paper in my hands. Oh! There's a back page. I read it. Oh! He likes to jump fences and can be destructive. Oh?! I said out loud. I looked back at him. He was biting his chain-link cage now. His little white teeth clamped onto the metal, a look of urgency on his face.

"Okay, don't worry, you're coming with me," I reassured him. I squatted down to look him in the eye, confirming we had already made a best friends pact.

That's how my sweet dog came to be with us. He's a good boy. Usually. He is fascinated by other animals and can get very excited, in an uncontrollable way, when he sees or smells them, but most particularly when they can be chased.

One day, his leash broke when he lunged after some deer. For a moment he didn't realize it, but then chooooooo—he was gone. He raced after the deer as fast as he could. I had no idea where he'd gone, it was so fast, a blur. I felt afraid and sick, like I wanted to cry and vomit and curl up in a little ball. I called him, rattled his cookie bag. Nothing. I went in the direction I'd seen him bolt. Nothing. I ran, calling, crackling that plastic cookie bag—his favorite sound. Nothing.

My mind raced with tragic scenarios. What if he gets hit by a car? Hurt in the forest? Shot by a hunter? What if I never find him? Never see my best friend again? It was a nightmare. At times like these when your heart is full of fear and your mind is racing with anxiety, helplessness, and hopelessness, it seems like forever, like *years* of pain and worry. In reality, maybe it was 15 minutes. Then I heard a commotion in the distance. I took the gravel road around to where I thought the noise was coming from. The noise was louder now, a mix of heavy breathing, squealing, slurping sounds. I went closer, not sure whether I was hoping those strange sounds involved my dog or not. I went closer. And closer. The sounds kept getting louder.

This is a sight I'll never forget. My 50-pound dog up to his chin in pig pen slop, trying his best to herd some pigs that were easily three times his size. He was so awkward and slow in that deep mud slop that there was no way he could herd or hurt the pigs. He's lucky they didn't sit on him and suffocate him in the slop. They easily could have done so. But they had mercy on my naughty dog that day. I was no longer terrified. What relief to find him. But how disgusting it looked. And smelled.

I'm grateful the smell is finally gone. But the lessons remain. My dog is my teacher. Here are some of the lessons he's brought to my life:

Live in the moment.

Don't give up; you never know when the leash might break.

Don't be afraid to try and herd someone three times your size.

And finally, a best friends pact means unconditional love, even when one of you smells like a pig pen.

Discussion/Journaling Questions for "Best Friends"

1. Think of someone who is a best friend. How did you meet? What is one difficulty you survived together? Think about how important friends are in helping you through the ups and downs of life. Make a plan to enjoy some time with a best friend today.

2. Dogs are famous for living in the moment. At which times are you best able to also live in the moment? Think about a specific time in which you really savored living in the moment. After you savor that memory, think of another time when you were worried about the future or feeling upset about the past. How are you different when you live in the moment versus not?

3. In "Best Friends," we see it is impossible for the dog to successfully herd the pigs. Yet he still tries and delights in the effort. What is an activity or accomplishment you believe to be "impossible" yet you still relish in the sheer effort of the attempt?

Mosquitos and Lemon Balm

I cannot really say I love mosquitos.

But they've taken so much of my blood over the years that I might be an honorary member of the mosquito family. They probably have tiny little hats they wear and a blood cake they eat to celebrate my birthday each year. Buzzing and humming the birthday tune and wishing me many more delicious years of life.

Perhaps they retell stories, times when an extra-large dose of my blood sustained them or their ancestors, maybe the times when I came through for them *just* when they needed it most. My uncovered arm or bug spray–less ankles a blessing to them. And they in turn are blessings to birds, fish, and other insects who rely on mosquitos as a food source.

One of their favorite stories may be the time

when I was in elementary school and attended one of my first sleepovers at a friend's house. It was summertime and a very busy time on the family farm, but I begged and pleaded and was allowed to go. My mom sent along a can of Deep Woods OFF! to help keep me safe from mosquitos, or so we thought.

I was dropped off at my friend's house and what a party! So many girls from school, most of whom I'd hardly seen over the summer. What fun we had running and playing. Then time to set up our sleeping bags. Shall we sleep inside on the floor? Or outside in tents? Oh! We'll all be outside. Except there is no tent. Only a huge tarp strung up. Open to bugs. Hmmm…ok. That's fine. I have my trusty OFF! It smells and stings and tastes as awful as you can chemically imagine, so it must be good. I followed instructions and covered my face with both hands as I was sprayed down. I still remember the shhhhhhhhhh of the can. That revolting smell.

Mostly covered in spray, I enjoyed the rest of the slumber party. Candy and popcorn and ghost stories (spooky)! I don't actually like spooky stories, but one must sometimes make an effort to fit in, you know. Eventually, all the girls fell asleep. I awoke in the morning feeling itchy and swollen. Uncomfortable.

I found my friend's mom, who looked at me with that adult expression of worry and fear and horror with a fake smile plastered over the top.

"Let's call your mom to come pick you up, sweetheart, okay?" in that I'm-trying-not-to-sound-worried-but-it's-not-working voice, usually an octave too high.

The call was made. Confirmation was received about medication. My friend's mom rummaged through her medicine cabinet for Benadryl and calamine lotion. That thick pink lotion was patted all over me but mostly on my face. A Benadryl capsule was swallowed. I didn't see myself in the mirror yet, but I could tell from the comments made by several people that I was looking horrible, scary like a Halloween mask.

My mom came to get me. On the way home, she grumbled about the mosquitos out there by Marion Drain, a large irrigation ditch on our reservation.

I easily had 80 mosquito bites, about 30 of which were on my face. Despite its chemical smell, the OFF! had not worked. Another thick layer of calamine lotion was applied, and I was sent to bed.

I didn't mind being bedridden that day, drowsy from the Benadryl and tired of hearing references to my Halloween-mask-like face. Through swollen eyes, I peeked into the mirror. I didn't recognize myself, my face puffy and lumpy, skin stretched to its limit.

I can imagine mosquitos recounting that story, clinking "Cheers!" with their goblets full of blood sloshing in celebration. Those little bugs that cause such big harm sometimes.

Reflecting now, I see they also teach.

I rarely appreciate having itch- and swollen-free skin...until I deal with the inconvenience of a mosquito bite.

They don't all bite. So, I need to remember they don't all cause pain—this reminds me to slow my judgment.

I love so many beautiful birds, fish, and other beings mosquitos feed. We're all interconnected and interdependent. These little insects, mosquitos, they help power the ecosystems I love best.

When I work at it, I have gratitude for mosquitos. And one thing I'm grateful for is that mosquitos don't like lemon balm. My garden overflows with this blessed plant, lemon balm, whose oil is in the non-toxic sprays and lotions I now use to prevent pesky bites.

I cannot say I *love* mosquitos, but through them I've learned a lot.

And I learned a love for lemon balm, my tangy, spunky plant sister with a strong spine and a zest for life.

She helps me and protects me, and I tend her in my garden.

She is a blessing.

Discussion/Journaling Questions for "Mosquitos and Lemon Balm"

1. Think of a trying time in your life when you learned something despite major or minor inconvenience. What did you learn?

2. In "Mosquitos and Lemon Balm," the narrator remembers being teased or insulted for her appearance. Think of a time when you experienced or witnessed teasing or insults. How did you respond? Would you respond similarly or differently now?

3. Mosquitos are largely viewed as pests, yet the narrator also sees how her gift of blood for them may be viewed differently. What is a current problem in your life that can be seen from different viewpoints or dimensions? Try to turn the problem over in your mind to see it from another perspective. How many different viewpoints can you imagine?

Spilyáy (Legendary Coyote)
Is a Feminist

My dog, like many rez dogs, I think is part coyote. He looks it, at certain times more than others, that gangly-legged appearance, wily look on his face, resembling his Looney Tunes relation. And why shouldn't he look like a coyote? Like our beloved dogs, coyotes have lived among our people Since Time Immemorial. When Coyote is in our traditional stories, his name is Spilyáy.

Legendary Coyote, Spilyáy, is one of our most famous teachers. He is the star of many Yakama stories, passed down through generations. Storytellers ensure we learn important lessons about how to conduct ourselves, and the stories help us address big questions: Why do we exist? Why does our Indigenous homeland look the way it does? What are our responsibilities to all of our relations, human and more than human?

Coyote is known as a trickster in stories from many cultures. Yet he's more than a tricky entertainer. He's a teacher. Yes, he blunders along, making mistakes and being prideful or greedy—sometimes to his demise. In this way, he reflects us human people in our daily blunders; he's a relatable teacher.

Our stories are often thought to be for children; however, wise adults and Elders seek them out. Even if someone has heard a story 150 times, there is a unique lesson embedded in the story— Spilyáy drops a nugget of wisdom or insight that is meant for each listener in *that* particular moment, so each listener may better themselves as a result. This is our traditional way of learning…of education: repetition, humility, observation, listening so deep it can touch your spirit.

There are many lessons Spilyáy teaches and models. Some are well known and discussed. Yet there is one I fear may be overlooked. Time after time, when Spilyáy is stumped or having difficulty, unsure of what to do, he often turns to his sisters for their wise counsel. For example, in the Legend about Pyaxí, Spilyáy learns from his sisters how to bring Pyaxí (bitterroot), one of our precious traditional foods, to the places our Yakama people now harvest this important food source. In the story, Spilyáy follows through on his sisters' instructions and in doing so addresses his own pitiful hunger, and he brings Pyax̱í to the places that will nourish generations of Yakama peoples.

Spilyáy's sisters know he's kind of a mess. He can be conceited and greedy and often after they help him with his deepest problems, he finds success...and then pretends he did it all on his own, not acknowledging his sisters' help. And then in his next problem, he turns to his sisters again. They tell him he's an ingrate, and he promises he'll acknowledge their assistance, their wisdom. And so it goes, the bickering of siblings that probably sounds familiar to us all.

I love Spilyáy because of the rich and beautiful contradictions he brings to our precious stories. Through his efforts and antics, we see the strong and steady presence as well as the necessity and importance of women's wisdom and power; his sisters' voices and teachings always provide the teachings needed, when they are needed most. Spilyáy leads us so we may grasp the lesson, if we so choose.

All of our traditional stories are meant to

help us humans, so that we may learn from our many blunders as we walk along our path of life. Our stories are gifts that keep on giving. We can turn the teachings from our stories over and over in our minds and hearts, having their lessons as company on our journey; they help us become stronger individuals who may help our greater collective.

I love our Coyote stories and the ways Spilyáy as both a trickster *and* a role model helps teach us. I love that Spilyáy helps us see how much folly can be avoided if women were truly respected and honored. Perhaps now more than ever we need these precious teachings in our communities, in our society. Spilyáy demonstrates a relational politics; feminism is a collective project, and Spilyáy models this time and again. I dare say—I believe Spilyáy is a feminist. And *that* would make his sisters proud.

Note: "Legend about Pyaxí" is more fully described in *Anakú Iwachá*, the treasured book of Yakama legends, in the 1974 edition. The legend is also included in the second edition of *Anakú Iwachá* (University of Washington Press, 2021).

Discussion/Journaling Questions for "Spilyáy (Legendary Coyote) Is a Feminist"

1. Coyote is a famous teacher and trickster. Think about a tricky lesson you learned. Who or what helped teach you that lesson?

2. Spilyáy (Legendary Coyote) often turns to his sisters for help and wise counsel. To whom do you turn to for help and wise counsel? Think of a situation in which you really needed help and someone came through to help you. Avoid being like conceited Spilyáy and write a little note of thanks to your wise helper(s). If possible, send the note to your helper(s).

3. Spilyáy is a male figure who helps teach us to value the power and importance of women. Think of a male figure in your life who truly respects and honors women. How does he show this in his daily life? What lessons can you learn from or how can you follow his good example?

Conclusion

As we've journeyed together through the stories in this book, we've touched on the sacredness of a creation story in which Salmon and Water offer themselves so humans may live and the profaneness of a dog covered in pig waste and mud.

We've considered the beauty of a Salmon dancing in a fishing net and the wilyness of a coyote who ultimately teaches us the power of women's wisdom.

We've learned about the sweet, tart, and strong characteristics in some of our more than human relations, like huckleberry, apple, carrot, ant, and lemon balm. We've gazed at flowers and plants and considered the personal and societal moral teachings that pretty yellow blooms and green and purple berries may teach us.

Whether we are harvesting in the foothills of the Yakama Reservation, standing near the coast of the Pacific Ocean with Southern California mission bells clanging in the background, cruising the I-84 freeway along the Columbia River, eating popcorn while camping in a friend's backyard, or harvesting ripe apples in fall, we are always invited to pause and notice the places and beings around us. It is then that we receive gifts, of connection to our inner wisdom and respectful relation to place.

With these gifts we learn how to be our best selves.

We have so many loving teachers all around us. Land and place are teachers and caretakers for us. Our more than human relatives stand always at the ready to help us on our path and to build a collective future in which we can all thrive. Like our beloved more than human relations, we are part of the interconnected and interdependent ecosystems we inhabit. What will our contributions be today?

Thank you for joining me along this journey with *Huckleberries and Coyotes: Lessons from Our More than Human Relations.*

I wish you a good continued journey as you connect more deeply with your own people's stories and find new stories that make you laugh heartily, think deeply, and contribute more generously to the collectives to which you belong.

About the Illustrator

Crystal L. Buck is a Native American artist and resides in Spokane, Washington. She is an enrolled member of the Yakama Nation and grew up on the Yakama Indian Reservation. Her passion for drawing and painting evolved at a very young age. She gives credit to her amazing art teachers. They encouraged her and believed in her talent enough to enter her work in local shows throughout the years. Before completing high school, she participated in her first painting showcase where she met and networked with various artists. She sold her first piece in 1997. Upon graduating from college as an Exercise Specialist in 2003, she also received a minor in art with a specialization in painting from Fort Lewis College in Durango, Colorado. Most recently, her drawing was selected for the 2019–2020 Washington State Indian Education

Program logo. In 2020, Crystal illustrated the book *The Auntie Way: Stories Celebrating Kindness, Fierceness, and Creativity.* Crystal is the mother of four beautiful children and loves spending time with her family. She enjoys participating in traditional gatherings and learning the Salish language with her kids. She's passionate about running, leading fitness dance classes, drawing, and crafting. She is inspired by artistic creations that focus on her Native roots, modern art techniques, Zentangle, vibrant and various uses of colors, lines, and patterns. One of her artistic dreams is to blend her love for hummingbirds and her individual style into a unique thematic masterpiece. You may contact Crystal by email: cry5tal_lea@yahoo.com

About the Author

Dr. Michelle M. Jacob is an enrolled member of the Yakama Nation and has over 20 years of teaching experience, most currently at the University of Oregon where she is Professor of Indigenous Studies in the Department of Education Studies, and serves as Affiliated Faculty in the Department of Indigenous, Race, and Ethnic Studies and in the Environmental Studies Program. Michelle engages in scholarly and activist work that seeks to understand and work toward a holistic sense of health and well-being within Indigenous communities and among allies who wish to engage decolonization. Michelle loves to write and has published five books, including *The Auntie Way* and *Yakama Rising*. She has also published numerous articles in social science, education, and health science research journals and has been awarded grants from the U.S.

Department of Education, the National Endowment for the Humanities, Spencer Foundation, and the National Science Foundation.Michelle founded Anahuy Mentoring, LLC, to support her vision of sharing Indigenous methodologies with a broad audience. Michelle is grateful to all her family and friends for their love and support and to her many blessed human and more than human relations who inspired *Huckleberries and Coyotes*.

You may contact Michelle through the form on her website, where you can also sign up for her email list to be the first to receive all the news related to Anahuy Mentoring https://anahuymentoring.com

Follow Michelle on Twitter: @AnahuyMentoring

Author Acknowledgments

I am grateful to the fantastic scholars and educators who peer-reviewed this book manuscript: Stephany RunningHawk Johnson, Kyle Whyte, Philip Deloria, Mercedes Jones, Regina Sievert, Tina Gutierez-Schmich, and Julia Heffernan. Leilani Sabzalian, Angie Morrill, Chris Andersen, and Theresa Jacob also offered valuable feedback on the manuscript. Thanks to Alja Kooistra for skillful copyediting. All feedback I received greatly strengthened this manuscript, and any weaknesses remain my own. I am grateful *Huckleberries and Coyotes* is blessed with the beautiful artwork of Crystal Buck. Thanks to all of the wonderful readers of my *The Auntie Way* blog and Anahuy Mentoring email subscribers, who chose the cover of *Huckleberries and Coyotes* through their collective voting.

I've been fortunate to work with many

supportive people who help me grow as a teacher, writer, and scholar—too many to name! I have wonderful colleagues at the University of Oregon College of Education, the Department of Education Studies, and my dear colleagues, students, and alums in our Sapsik'ʷałá Program. Thanks to the COE Finance team for their kindness and efficiency. The University of Oregon has a critical mass of outstanding Indigenous scholars and allies who are working on behalf of Tribal peoples; thanks to my colleagues in the Sapsik'ʷałá (Teacher) Education Program, Native American Studies Program, Northwest Indian Language Institute, and the Native Strategies Group. Thank you to the Whitefish Writers Circle and the many wonderful writers at Flathead Valley Community College.

In preparing this book, I was greatly inspired by the work I did with Virginia Beavert, Joana Jansen, and Deward Walker for the new edition of *Anakú Iwachá*, a tremendously important book of Yakama legends and stories that will be published in early 2021. Working on the *Anakú Iwachá* project helped remind me of the power of stories and the debt of gratitude I have to my Elders and all of my relations, human and more than human. It also made me reflect on the master storytellers I'm so grateful to have had in my life, including some of the folks I write about in *Huckleberries and Coyotes*—there are many—I'm so lucky!

Huge thanks to my family who have given me so much love and encouragement over the years and who model the love and care that our stories inspire: Dad, Mom, Uncle Jim, Roger, Gina, Garret, Hunter, Faith, Justin, Alicia, Quintic, Hazen, Blaise, Sealy, and my in-laws, who are a blessing!

I'll end by thanking the world's greatest camping buddies, Chris and Anahuy. Áwna! For reals.

About Anahuy Mentoring

Anahuy Mentoring is committed to engaging Indigenous methodologies to teach about the importance of Indigenous ways of knowing and being. *Huckleberries and Coyotes* is published by Anahuy Mentoring, an independent Indigenous press that utilizes Indigenous cultural values in peer review. Anahuy is the Yakama Ichishkíin word for black bear.

Learn more, sign up for courses, buy autographed books, purchase and send Auntie Grams, and join the email list at **https://anahuymentoring.com**

Twitter: @AnahuyMentoring

ANAHUY MENTORING, LLC
EXCELLENCE IN INDIGENOUS METHODS

The Auntie Way

Stories Celebrating Kindness, Fierceness, and Creativity

Michelle M. Jacob

Also available from Anahuy Mentoring:
The Auntie Way
The Auntie Way celebrates the love and lessons we
learn from our favorite aunts, whether related or
chosen, and is available in paperback and e-book
from Amazon or your favorite bookstore. You
may purchase author autographed copies of *The
Auntie Way* at https://anahuymentoring.com
Aunties are awesome!

Made in United States
Troutdale, OR
12/14/2023

15849120R00072